Golden Slippers

Golden Slippers

*An Anthology of Negro Poetry
for Young Readers*

Compiled by
ARNA *Wendell* BONTEMPS

With Drawings by
HENRIETTA BRUCE SHARON

HARPER & BROTHERS PUBLISHERS
New York and London

To JOAN and PAUL

Who Helped

CONTENTS

[vii]

[ix]

[x]

[xi]

I. Waking Up

Dawn

An ANGEL, robed in spotless white,
Bent down and kissed the sleeping Night.
Night woke to blush; the sprite was gone.
Men saw the blush and called it Dawn.

Paul Laurence Dunbar

"I Am Glad Daylong"

I AM glad daylong for the gift of song,
For time and change and sorrow;
For the sunset wings and the world-end things
Which hang on the edge of tomorrow.
I am glad for my heart whose gates apart
Are the entrance-place of wonders,
Where dreams come in from the rush and din
Like sheep from the rains and thunders.

William Stanley Braithwaite

In the Morning

'Lias! 'Lias! Bless de Lawd!
Don' you know de day's erbroad?
Ef you don' git up, you scamp,
Dey'll be trouble in dis camp.
T'ink I gwine to let you sleep
W'ile I meks yo' boa'd an' keep?
Dat's a putty howdy-do—
Don' you hyeah me, 'Lias—you?

Bet ef I come crost dis flo'
You won' fin' no time to sno'.
Daylight all a-shinin' in
W'ile you sleep—w'y hit's a sin!
Ain't de can'le-light enough
To bu'n out widout a snuff,
But you go de mo'nin' thoo
Bu'in' up de daylight too?

'Lias, don' you hyeah me call?
No use tu'nin' to'ds de wall;
I kin hyeah dat mattuss squeak;
Don' you hyeah me w'en I speak?
Dis hyeah clock done struck off six—
Ca'line, bring me dem ah sticks!
Oh, you down, suh; huh, you down—
Look hyeah, don' you daih to frown.

Ma'ch yo' se'f an' wash yo' face,
Don' you splattah all de place;
I got somep'n else to do,
'Sides jes' cleanin' aftah you.
Tek dat comb an' fix yo' haid—
Looks jes' lak a feddah baid.
Look hyeah, boy, I let you see
You sha'n't roll yo' eyes at me.

Come hyeah; bring me dat ah strap!
Boy, I'll whup you 'twell you drap;
You done felt yo'se'f too strong,
An' you sholy got me wrong.
Set down at dat table thaih;
Jes' you whimpah ef you daih!
Evah mo'nin' on dis place
Seem lak I mus' lose my grace.

Fol' yo' han's an' bow yo' haid—
Wait ontwell de blessin' 's said;
"Lawd, have mussy on ouah souls—"
(Don' you daih to tech dem rolls—)
"Bless de food we gwine to eat—"
(You set still—I see yo' feet;
You jes' try dat trick agin!)
"Gin us peace an' joy. Amen!"

Paul Laurence Dunbar

[6]

Midsummer Morn

A TOM-TOM sun awakens day's jungle with heat beats
The moon was a white war canoe moored to the night
Morning stars scurry to cover like shaking hares fearful
    of the Great Yellow Hunter
Last night's tall hunchback fishing in a pool of raven's
    breasts is a green elm tree
Thin wings of grass pound helplessly against hard
    ground
And the robins are no longer afraid. . . .

Frank Marshall Davis

Sassafras Tea

THE sassafras tea is red and clear
    In my white china cup,
So pretty I keep peeping in
    Before I drink it up.

I stir it with a silver spoon,
    And sometimes I just hold
A little tea inside the spoon,
    Like it was lined with gold.

It makes me hungry just to smell
    The nice hot sassafras tea,
And that's one thing I really like
    That they say's good for me.

Mary Effie Lee Newsome

Youth

WE HAVE tomorrow
Bright before us
Like a flame.

Yesterday
A night-gone thing,
A sun-down name.

And dawn-today
Broad arch above the road we came.

We march!

Langston Hughes

II. Playtime

Did You Feed My Cow?

"DID you feed my cow?"
  "Yes, Mam!"
"Will you tell me how?"
  "Yes, Mam!"
"Oh, what did you give her?"
  "Corn an' hay."
"Oh, what did you give her?"
  "Corn an' hay."

"Did you milk her good?"
  "Yes, Mam!"
"Did you do like you should?"
  "Yes, Mam!"
"Oh, how did you milk her?"
  "Swish! Swish! Swish!"
"Oh, how did you milk her?"
  "Swish! Swish! Swish!"

"Did that cow die?"
  "Yes, Mam!"
"With a pain in her eye?"
  "Yes, Mam!"
"Oh, how did she die?"
  "Uh! Uh! Uh!"
"Oh, how did she die?"
  "Uh! Uh! Uh!"

"Did the buzzards come?"
  "Yes, Mam!"
"For to pick her bone?"
  "Yes, Mam!"
"Oh, how did they come?"
  "Flop! Flop! Flop!"
"Oh, how did they come?"
  "Flop! Flop! Flop!"

Traditional

Bedbug

THE June-bug's got the golden wing,
  The Lightning-bug the flame;
The Bedbug's got no wing at all,
  But he gets there just the same.

The Pumpkin-bug's got a pumpkin smell,
  The Squash-bug smells the worst;
But the perfume of that old Bedbug,
  It's enough to make you burst.

When that Bedbug come down to my house,
  I takes my walking cane.
Go get a pot and scald him hot!
  Good-by, Miss Liza Jane!

Traditional

Precious Things

HOLD my rooster, hold my hen,
Pray don't touch my Grecian Bend.

Hold my bonnet, hold my shawl,
Pray don't touch my waterfall.

Hold my hands by the finger tips,
But pray don't touch my sweet little lips.

Traditional

I'm a Round-Town Gent

I AIN'T no wagon, ain't no dray,
Just come to town with a load of hay.
I ain't no cornfield to go to bed
With a lot of hayseeds in my head.
I'm a round-town gent, and I don't choose
To work in the mud and do without shoes.

Traditional

Take Yo' Time, Miss Lucy

MISS LUCY she is handsome,
  Miss Lucy she is tall;
To see her dance Cachuca,
  Jes' captivates us all.

Oh, Miss Lucy's teeth is grinnin',
  Jes' like an ear of corn;
An' her eyes dey look so winnin',
  Oh! would I'd never been born.

Take yo' time, Miss Lucy,
  Take yo' time, Miss Lucy Long;
Oh! take yo' time, Miss Lucy,
  Take yo' time, Miss Lucy Long.

I ax'd her for to marry
  Myself de other day;
She said she'd rather tarry,
  So I let her have her way.

If she makes a scolding wife,
  As sure as she is born,
I'll tote her down to Georgia,
  An' trade her off for corn.

Take yo' time, Miss Lucy,
    Take yo' time, Miss Lucy Long;
Oh! take yo' time, Miss Lucy,
    Take yo' time, Miss Lucy Long.

Traditional

Quoits

IN WINTERTIME I have such fun
   When I play quoits with father.
I beat him almost every game.
   He never seems to bother.

He looks at mother and just smiles.
   All this seems strange to me,
For when he plays with grown-up folks,
   He beats them easily.

Mary Effie Lee Newsome

III. Clothes Lines and Water Pails

Signs

I'M SURE that Spring is on the way.
　My Ma gave me a sign.
She swept the heavy rugs today
　And hung them on the line.

Beatrice M. Murphy

The Baker's Boy

THE baker's boy delivers loaves
All up and down our street.
His car is white, his clothes are white,
White to his very feet.
I wonder if he stays that way.
I don't see how he does all day.
I'd like to watch him going home
When all the loaves are out.
His clothes must look quite different then,
At least I have no doubt.

Mary Effie Lee Newsome

The Serving Girl

THE calabash wherein she served my food,
Was smooth and polished as sandalwood:
Fish, as white as the foam of the sea,
Peppered, and golden fried for me.
She brought palm wine that carelessly slips
From the sleeping palm tree's honeyed lips.
But who can guess, or even surmise.
The countless things she served with her eyes?

Gladys May Casely Hayford

No Images

She does not know
Her beauty,
She thinks her brown body
Has no glory.

If she could dance
Under palm trees
And see her image in the river
She would know.

But there are no palm trees
On the street,
And dish water gives back no images.

Waring Cuney

I've Learned to Sing

I'VE learned to sing a song of hope,
I've said goodbye to despair,
I caught the note in a thrush's throat,
I sang—and the world was fair!
I've learned to sing a song of joy
It bends the skies to me,
The song of joy is the song of hope
Grown to maturity.

I've learned to laugh away my tears
As through the dark I go
For love and laughter conquer fears
My heart has come to know.

I've learned a song of happiness
It is a song of love
For love alone is happiness
And happiness is love.

Georgia Douglas Johnson

IV. Hard Work

Florida Road Workers

I'M MAKIN' a road
For the cars to fly by on,
Makin' a road
Through the palmetto thicket
For light and civilization
To travel on.
I'm makin' a road
For the rich old white men
To sweep over in their big cars
And leave me standin' here.

Sure,
A road helps everybody!
Rich folks ride—
And I get to see 'em ride.
I ain't never seen nobody
Ride so fine before.

Hey, buddy!
Look at me!
I'm makin' a road!

Langston Hughes

John Henry

SOME say he's from Georgia,
Some say he's from Alabam,
But it's wrote on the rock at the Big Ben Tunnel,
That he's an East Virginia man,
That he's an East Virginia man.

John Henry was a steel drivin' man,
He died with a hammah in his han',
Oh, come along boys and line the track
For John Henry ain't never comin' back,
For John Henry ain't never comin' back.

John Henry he could hammah,
He could whistle, he could sing,
He went to the mountain early in the mornin'
To hear his hammah ring,
To hear his hammah ring.

John Henry went to the section boss,
Says the sections boss what kin you do?
Says I can line a track, I kin histe a jack,
I kin pick and shovel too,
I kin pick and shovel too.

John Henry told the cap'n,
When you go to town,

Buy me a nine-pound hammah
An' I'll drive this steel drill down,
An' I'll drive this steel drill down.

Cap'n said to John Henry
You've got a willin' mind.
But you just well lay yoh hammah down,
You'll nevah beat this drill of mine,
You'll nevah beat this drill of mine.

John Henry went to the tunnel
And they put him in lead to drive,
The rock was so tall and John Henry so small
That he laid down his hammah and he cried,
That he laid down his hammah and he cried.

The steam drill was on the right han' side,
John Henry was on the left,
Says before I let this steam drill beat me down,
I'll hammah myself to death,
I'll hammah myself to death.

Oh the cap'n said to John Henry
I bleeve this mountain's sinkin' in.
John Henry said to the cap'n, Oh my!
Tain't nothin' but my hammah suckin' wind,
Tain't nothin' but my hammah suckin' wind.

John Henry had a cute liddle wife,
And her name was Julie Ann,
And she walk down the track and nevah look back,
Goin' to see her brave steel drivin' man,
Goin' to see her brave steel drivin' man.

John Henry was on the mountain,
The mountain was so high,
He called to his pretty liddle wife,
Said Ah kin almos' touch the sky,
Said Ah kin almos' touch the sky.

John Henry took his liddle boy,
Sit him on his knee,
Said that Big Ben Tunnel
Gonna be the death of me,
Gonna be the death of me.

John Henry ast that liddle boy,
Now what are you gonna be?
Says if I live and nothin' happen,
A steel drivin' man I'll be,
A steel drivin' man I'll be.

Then John Henry he did hammah,
He did make his hammah soun',
Says now one more lick fore quittin' time,
An' I'll beat this steam drill down,
An' I'll beat this steam drill down.

John Henry, O, John Henry!
Blood am runnin' red!
Falls right down with his hammah to the groun',
Says, I've beat him to the bottom but I'm dead,
I've beat him to the bottom but I'm dead.

John Henry, O, John Henry!
Sing it if you can,—
High and low and ev'ry where you go—
He died with his hammah in his han',
He died with his hammah in his han'.

They took John Henry to the White House,
And buried him in the san',
And every locomotive come roarin' by,
Says there lays that steel drivin' man,
Says there lays that steel drivin' man.

Traditional

John Henry in Harlem

The scabby walls of tenements
Tower on either hand
Like the wind-clawed sides
Of a Dust Bowl canyon.

In the dream-dead street
The heat waves dance
Like ghosts upon a plagued river.

Stripped to the waist,
His muscles knotted like ebony cords,
Stillicho swings his mighty pick
And his lusty ballad of John Henry
Climbs the fire-trap tenements:

John Henry said: "If you give me a drink
I'll finish dis job befo' a cat kin wink.
When Gawd made me, He made a man
Who's de best pick driver in all de lan'."

The sweat rolls down Stillicho's body,
And the sweat rolls down his face,
And the blur of the street scene wavers before his eyes,
And the rag of the toiler wipes his face.

Stillicho thinks of his wife,
The big pot of cabbage and ham-hock
Waiting for him in the flat.

He sees pride shining in her eyes
When he brings home his check, Saturday nights,
And hides it where she can find it.

John Henry he had a pretty wife,
An' her name it was Polly Ann.
She loved her home an' she loved her kid
An' she loved her pickdrivin' man!

Stillicho Spikes dreams of his son
And the bright new watch he'll buy the lad
When he finishes high school in June,
The first of the Spikes to get a diploma.
Didn't the principal say
Junior was smart
And perhaps he'd be a second Booker T.?

John Henry he had a little boy,
An' he was John Henry's pride an' joy.
John Henry said, "He'll make a man
As good as any in dis wide, wide lan'."

The verve of his thoughts
Makes his pick rise and fall
Like the regal stick of a drum-major.

Stillicho looks at the slanting sun,
Spits on his horny hands,
Rubs them and grins.

John Henry worked in all kinds of weather,
'Cause a workin' man cain't do no better.
John Henry said to just keep in motion
Till you conquer de lan' an' conquer de ocean!

M. B. Toleson

Song to a Negro Wash-Woman

OH, WASH-WOMAN,
Arms elbow-deep in white suds,
Soul washed clean,
Clothes washed clean,
I have many songs to sing you
Could I but find the words.

Was it four o'clock or six o'clock on a winter afternoon,
    I saw you wringing out the last shirt in Miss White
    Lady's kitchen? Was it four o'clock or six o'clock?
    I don't remember.

But I know, at seven one spring morning you were on
    Vermont Street with a bundle in your arms going to
    wash clothes.

And I know I've seen you in the New York subway in
    the late afternoon coming home from washing clothes.

Yes, I know you, wash-woman.

I know how you send your children to school, and
    high school, and even college.
I know how you work to help your man when times
    are hard.
I know how you build your house up from the washtub
    and call it home.

And how you raise your churches from white suds for
the service of the Holy God.

I've seen you singing, wash-woman. Out in the back-
yard garden under the apple trees, singing, hanging
white clothes on long lines in the sunshine.
And I've seen you in church on Sunday morning singing, praising your Jesus because some day you're
going to sit on the right hand side of the Son of
God and forget you ever were a wash-woman.
And the aching back and the bundles of clothes will be
unremembered then.

Yes, I've seen you singing.

So for you,
O singing wash-woman,
For you, singing little brown woman,
Singing strong black woman,
Singing tall yellow woman,
Arms deep in white suds,
Soul washed clean,
Clothes washed clean,
For you I have
Many songs to sing
Could I but find the words.

Langston Hughes

[42]

MERRY voices chatterin',
Nimble feet dem patterin',
Big an' little, faces gay,
Happy day dis market day.

Sateday, de marnin' break,
Soon, soon market-people wake;
An' de light shine from de moon
While dem boy, wid pantaloon
Roll up over dem knee-pan,
'Tep across de buccra lan'
To de pastur' whe' de harse
Feed along wid de jackass,
An' de mule cant' in de track
Wid him tail up in him back,
All de ketchin' to defy,
No ca' how dem boy might try.

In de early marnin'-tide,
When de cocks crow on de hill
An' de stars are shinin' still,
Mirrie by de fireside
Hot's de coffee for de lads
Comin' ridin' on de pads
T'rown across dem animul—
Donkey, harse too, an' de mule,

Which at last had come do'n cool.
On de bit dem hol' dem full:
Racin' ober pastur' lan',
See dem comin' ebery man,
Comin' fe de steamin' tea
Ober hilly track an' lea.

Hard-wuk'd donkey on de road
Trottin' wid him ushal load,
Hamper pack' wi' yam an' grain,
Sour-sop, and Gub'nor cane.

Cous' Sun sits in hired dray,
Drivin' 'long de market way;
Whole week grindin' sugar cane
T'rough de boilin' sun an' rain,
Now, a'ter de toilin' hard,
He goes seekin' his reward,
While he's thinkin' in him min'
Of de dear ones lef' behin',
Of de loved though ailin' wife,
Darlin' treasure of his life,
An' de picknies, six in all,
Whose 'nuff burdens 'pon him fall:
Seben lovin' ones in need,
Seben hungry mouths te feed;
On deir wants he thinks alone,
Neber dreamin' of his own,

But gwin' on wid joyful face
Till him re'ch de market-place.

Sugar bears no price today,
Though it is de mont' o' May,
When de time is hellish hot,
An' de water cocoanut
An' de cane bebridge is nice,
Mix' up wid a lilly ice.

Big an' little, great an' small,
Afou yam is all de call;
Sugar tup an' gill a quart,
Yet de people hab de heart
Wantin' brater top o' i',
Want de sweatin' higgler fe
Ram de pan an' pile i' up,
Yet sell i' fe so-so tup.

Cousin Sun is lookin' sad,
As de market is so bad;
'Pon him han' him res' him chin,
Quietly sit do'n thinkin'
Of de loved wife sick in bed,
An' de children to be fed—
What de laborers would say
When dem know him couldn' pay;
Also what about de mill

Whe' him hire from old Bill;
So him think, an' think on so,
Till him t'oughts no more could go.

Then he got up an' began
Pickin' up him sugar-pan:
In his ears rang t'rough de din
"Only two-an'-six a tin'."
What a tale he'd got to tell,
How bad, bad de sugar sell!
Tekin' out de lee amount,
Him set do'n an' begin count
All de time him min' deh doubt
How expenses would pay out;
Ah, it gnawed him like de ticks,
Sugar sell fe two-an'-six!

So he journeys on de way,
Feelin' sad dis market day;
No e'en buy a little cake
To gi'e baby when she wake—
Passin' 'long de candy-shop
'Douten eben mek a stop
To buy drops fe las'y son,
For de lilly cash nea' done.
So him re'ch him own a groun',
An' de children scamper roun',

Each one stretchin' out him han',
Lookin' to de poor, sad man.

Oh, how much he felt de blow,
As he watched dem face fall low,
When dem wait an' nuttin' came,
An' drew back deir han's wid shame!
But de sick wife kissed his brow:
"Sun, don't get down-hearted now;
Ef we only pay expense
We mus' wuk we common-sense,
Cut an' carve, an' carve an' cut,
Mek gill sarbe fe quattiwut;
We mus' try mek two ends meet
Neber mind how hard be it.
We won't mind de haul an' pull,
While dem pickny belly full."

An' de shadow lef' him face,
An' him felt an inward peace,
As he blessed his better part
For her sweet an' gentle heart:
"Dear one o' my heart, my breat',
Won't I lub you to de deat'?
When my heart is weak an' sad,
Who but you can mek it glad?"

So dey kissed an' kissed again,
An' deir t'oughts were not on pain,
But was 'way down in de sout'
Where dey'd wedded in deir yout',
In de marnin' of deir life
Free from all de grief an' strife,
Happy in de marnin' light,
Never thinkin' of de night.

So dey k'lated eberyt'ing;
An' de profit it could bring,
A'ter all de business fix',
Was a princely two-an'-six.

Claude McKay

Tomorrow's Men

CHILDREN today—tomorrow—men!
A few more suns and moons and then
Long limbed and sinewy they stand
The manhood of our native land.

Show them the dignity of toil;
Give them the mother-touch of soil;
Teach them the cunning of the tool;
As well as riddles of the school.

For wealth and favors fade away
With fortune's frown within a day;
But masters of a trade are free
To re-secure their destiny.

Where is the man who dares to scorn
The honest man to labor born?
For Labor has her rugged peers
Who glorify the gown she wears!

Georgia Douglas Johnson

The Negro Speaks of Rivers

I'vE known rivers:
I've known rivers ancient as the world and older than
    the flow of human blood in human veins.

My soul has grown deep like the rivers.

I bathed in the Euphrates when dawns were young.
I built my hut near the Congo and it lulled me to sleep.
I looked upon the Nile and raised the pyramids above it.
I heard the singing of the Mississippi when Abe Lincoln
    went down to New Orleans, and I've seen its
    muddy bosom turn all golden in the sunset.

I've known rivers:
Ancient, dusky rivers.

    My soul has grown deep like the rivers.

Langston Hughes

V. Chariot Wheels

The Creation

(A Negro Sermon)

And God stepped out on space,
And he looked around and said:
I'm lonely—
I'll make me a world.

And far as the eye of God could see
Darkness covered everything,
Blacker than a hundred midnights
Down in a cypress swamp.

Then God smiled,
And the light broke,
And the darkness rolled up on one side,
And the light stood shining on the other,
And God said: That's good!

Then God reached out and took the light in His hands,
And God rolled the light around in His hands
Until He made the sun;
And He set that sun a-blazing in the heavens.
And the light that was left from making the sun
God gathered it up in a shining ball
And flung it against the darkness,
Spangling the night with the moon and stars.
Then down between

The darkness and the light
He hurled the world;
And God said: That's good!

Then God himself stepped down—
And the sun was on His right hand,
And the moon was on His left;
The stars were clustered about His head,
And the earth was under His feet.
And God walked, and where He trod
His footsteps hollowed the valleys out
And bulged the mountains up.

Then He stopped and looked and saw
That the earth was hot and barren.
So God stepped over to the edge of the world
And He spat out the seven seas—
He batted his eyes, and the lightnings flashed—
He clapped His hands, and the thunders rolled—
And the waters above the earth came down,
The cooling waters came down.

Then the green grass sprouted,
And the little red flowers blossomed,
The pine tree pointed his finger to the sky,
And the oak spread out his arms,
The lakes cuddled down in the hollows of the ground,
And the rivers ran down to the sea;

And God smiled again,
And the rainbow appeared,
And curled itself around His shoulder.

Then God raised His arm and He waved His hand
Over the sea and over the land,
And He said: Bring forth! Bring forth!
And quicker than God could drop His hand,
Fishes and fowls
And beasts and birds
Swam the rivers and the seas,
Roamed the forests and the woods,
And split the air with their wings.
And God said: That's good!

Then God walked around,
And God looked around
On all that He had made.
He looked at His sun,
And He looked at His moon,
And He looked at His little stars;
He looked on His world
With all its living things,
And God said: I'm lonely still.

Then God sat down—
On the side of a hill where He could think;
By a deep, wide river He sat down;

With His head in His hands,
God thought and thought,
Till He thought: I'll make me a man!

Up from the bed of the river
God scooped the clay;
And by the bank of the river
He kneeled Him down;
And there the great God Almighty
Who lit the sun and fixed it in the sky,
Who flung the stars to the most far corner of the night,
Who rounded the earth in the middle of His hand;
This Great God,
Like a mammy bending over her baby,
Kneeled down in the dust
Toiling over a lump of clay
Till He shaped it in His own image;

Then into it He blew the breath of life,
And man became a living soul.
Amen. Amen.

James Weldon Johnson

Troubled Jesus

MA JESUS
Was a troubled man,
Wid lots o' sorrow
In His breast.
Oh, He was weary
When they laid Him
In the tomb to rest.
Po', good Jesus.

Waring Cuney

Crucifixion

THEY howled 'til Pilate
Sent dear Jesus out.
Then they cursed Him
An' knocked Him all about.

O brothers, O sisters,
Think what those sinners done—
Crucified the Lord's Son!
Think, think . . . Oh, think . . . .

Waring Cuney

Swing Low, Sweet Chariot

I LOOKED over Jordan, and what did I see
    Coming for to carry me home?
A band of angels coming after me,
    Coming for to carry me home.

Oh, if you get there before I do,
    Coming for to carry me home,
Tell all my friends I'm coming too,
    Coming for to carry me home.

Swing low, Sweet Chariot,
Coming for to carry me home.
Swing low, Sweet Chariot,
Coming for to carry me home.

Traditional

The Gospel Train

THE gospel train's a-coming,
    I hear it just at hand,
I hear the car wheels moving
    And rumbling through the land.

    Get on board, little chillun,
    Get on board, little chillun,
    Get on board, little chillun,
        There's room for many a mo'.

The fare is cheap and all can go,
    The rich and poor are there.
No second class aboard this train,
    No difference in the fare.

    Get on board, little chillun,
    Get on board, little chillun,
    Get on board, little chillun,
        There's room for many a mo'.

Traditional

Little David, Play on Yo' Harp

LITTLE David was a shepherd boy,
He killed Goliath and shouted for joy.

Little David, play on yo' harp,
Hallelu, hallelu!
Little David, play on yo' harp,
Hallelu!

Joshua was the son of Nun,
He never would stop till the work was done.

Little David, play on yo' harp,
Hallelu, hallelu!
Little David, play on yo' harp,
Hallelu!

Traditional

Ma Lord

MA LORD ain't no stuck-up man.
Ma Lord, he ain't proud.
When he goes a-walkin'
He gives me his hand.
"You ma friend," he 'lowed.

Ma Lord knowed what it was to work.
He knowed how to pray.
Ma Lord's life was trouble, too,
Trouble every day.

Ma Lord ain't no stuck-up man.
He's a friend o' mine.
When He went to Heaben,
His soul on fire,
He tole me I was gwine.
He said, "Sho you'll come wid Me
An' be ma friend through eternity."

Langston Hughes

Who Is That A-Walking in the Corn?

Who is that a-walking in the corn?
I have looked to East and looked to West
But nowhere could I find Him who walks
   Master's cornfield in the morning.

Who is that a-walking in the corn?
Is it Joshua, the son of Nun?—
Or King David come to fight the giant
   Near the cornfield in the morning ?

Who is that a-walking in the corn?
Is it Peter jangling Heaven's keys?—
Or old Gabriel come to blow his horn
   Near the cornfield in the morning?

Who is that a-walking in the corn?
I have looked to East and looked to West
But nowhere could I find Him who walks
   Master's cornfield in the morning.

Fenton Johnson

The Lonely Mother

Oh, MY mother's moaning by the river,
My poor mother's moaning by the river,
For her son who walks the earth in sorrow.
Long my mother's moaned beside the river,
And her tears have filled an angel's pitcher:
"Lord of Heaven, bring to me my honey,
Bring to me the darling of my bosom,
For a lonely mother by the river."

Cease, O mother, moaning by the river;
Cease, good mother, moaning by the river.
I have seen the star of Michael shining,
Michael shining at the Gates of Morning.
Row, O mighty angel, down the twilight,
Row until I find a lonely woman,
Swaying long beneath a tree of cypress,
Swaying for her son who walks in sorrow.

Fenton Johnson

For My Grandmother

THIS lovely flower fell to seed;
Work gently sun and rain;
She held it as her dying creed
That she would grow again.

Countee Cullen

Miracles

Doubt no longer miracles,
This spring day makes it plain
A man may crumble into dust
And straightway live again.

A jug of water in the sun
Will easy turn to wine
If love is stopping at the well
And love's brown arms entwine.

And you who think him only man,
I tell you faithfully
That I have seen Christ clothed in rain
Walking on the sea.

Arna Bontemps

Lift Every Voice and Sing

LIFT every voice and sing
Till earth and heaven ring,
Ring with the harmonies of Liberty;
Let our rejoicing rise
High as the listening skies,
Let it resound loud as the rolling sea.
Sing a song full of the faith that the dark past has taught
    us,
Sing a song full of the hope that the present has brought
    us,
Facing the rising sun of our new day begun
Let us march on till victory is won.

Stony the road we trod,
Bitter the chastening rod,
Felt in the days when hope unborn had died;
Yet with a steady beat,
Have not our weary feet
Come to the place for which our fathers sighed?
We have come over a way that with tears has been
    watered,
We have come, treading our path through the blood of
    the slaughtered,
Out from the gloomy past,
Till now we stand at last
Where the white gleam of our bright star is cast.

God of our weary years,
God of our silent tears,
Thou who hast brought us thus far on the way;
Thou who hast by Thy might
Led us into the light,
Keep us forever in the path, we pray.
Lest our feet stray from the places, our God, where we
    met Thee,
Lest, our hearts drunk with the wine of the world, we
    forget Thee;
Shadowed beneath Thy hand,
May we forever stand.
True to our God,
True to our native land.

James Weldon Johnson

VI. Feeling Blue

Carry Me Back to Old Virginny

CARRY me back to old Virginny,
There's where the cotton and the corn and 'tatoes grow,
There's where the birds warble sweet in the Springtime,
There's where the old darky's heart am long'd to go.
There's where I labor'd so hard for old Massa,
Day after day in the field of yellow corn,
No place on earth do I love more sincerely
Than old Virginny, the state where I was born.

Carry me back to old Virginny,
There let me live till I wither and decay,
Long by the old Dismal Swamp have I wandered,
There's where the old darky's life will pass away.
Massa and Missus have long gone before me,
Soon we will meet on that bright and golden shore,
There we'll be happy and free from all sorrow,
There's where we'll meet and we'll never part no more.

James A. Bland

Spring in New Hampshire

Too green the springing April grass,
Too blue the silver-speckled sky,
For me to linger here, alas,
While happy winds go laughing by,
Wasting the golden hours indoors,
Washing windows and scrubbing floors.

Too wonderful the April night,
Too faintly sweet the first May flowers,
The stars too gloriously bright,
For me to spend the evening hours,
When fields are fresh and streams are leaping,
Wearied, exhausted, dully sleeping.

Claude McKay

The Cricket and the Star

I HEAR the little black cricket,
I see the little white star.
The star looks very small to me
Because it is so far.
If the cricket were that far way
I'd never hear it night or day.

Mary Effie Lee Newsome

Home Thoughts

OH SOMETHING just now must be happening there!
That suddenly and quiveringly here,
Amid the city's noises, I must think
Of mangoes leaning o'er the river's brink,
And dexterous Davie climbing high above,
The gold fruits ebon-speckled to remove,
And toss them quickly in the tangled mass
Of wis-wis twisted round the guinea grass;
And Cyril coming through the bramble-track
A prize bunch of bananas on his back;
And Georgie—none could ever dive like him—
Throwing his scanty clothes off for a swim;
And schoolboys, from Bridge-tunnel going home,
Watching the waters downward dash and foam.
This is no daytime dream, there's something in it,
Oh something's happening there this very minute!

Claude McKay

Youth

THE dew is on the grasses, dear,
   The blush is on the rose,
And swift across our dial-youth,
   A shifting shadow goes.

The primrose moments, lush with bliss,
   Exhale and fade away,
Life may renew the Autumn time,
   But nevermore the May!

Georgia Douglas Johnson

Four-Leaf Clover

WHEN walking through the woods,
So many times I think I've found a four-leaf clover.
But like a dream—I stoop to find the dream is over—
It's a three.

It does not hurt me in the woods—
And would that when in life I've found a three-leaf
   clover,
And thought a four I would be able to discover,
Resigned I'll be. . . .

Wesley Curtright

VII. Brown Boy and Girl

Under the Mistletoe

I DID not know she'd take it so,
   Or else I'd never dared;
Although the bliss was worth the blow,
I did not know she'd take it so.
She stood beneath the mistletoe
So long I thought she cared;
I did not know she'd take it so,
Or else I'd never dared.

Countee Cullen

Heart of the Woods

DEEP into the woods we'll go,
Hand in hand.
Let the woods close about us,
Let the world outside be lost—
And let us find that Secret City
Lost so long ago—
In the Heart of the Woods.

Wesley Curtright

Li'l' Gal

Oh, DE weathah it is balmy an' de breeze is sighin' low.
      Li'l' gal,
An' de mockin' bird is singin' in de locus' by de do',
      Li'l' gal;
Dere's a hummin' an' a bummin' in de lan' f'om eas' to
   wes',
I's a-sighin' fu' you, honey, an' I nevah know no res'.
Fu' dey's lots o' trouble brewin' an' a-stewin in my breas',
      Li'l' gal.

Whut's de mattah wid de weathah, whut's de mattah
   wid de breeze,
      Li'l' gal?
Whut's de mattah wid de locus' dat's a-singin' in de
   trees,
      Li'l' gal?

W'y dey knows dey ladies love 'em an' dey knows dey
   love 'em true,
An' dey love 'em back, I reckon, des' lak I's a-lovin' you;
Dat's de reason dey's a-weavin' an' a-sighin', thoo an'
   thoo,
      Li'l' gal.

Don't you let no da'ky fool you 'cause de clo'es he waihs
   is fine,
             Li'l' gal.
Dey's a hones' hea't a-beatin' unnerneaf dese rags o'
   mine,
             Li'l' gal.
Cose dey ain't no use in mockin' whut de birds an'
   weathah do,
But I's so'y I cain't 'spress it w'en I knows I loves you
   true,
Dat's de reason I's a-sighin' an' a-singin' now fu' you,
             Li'l' gal.

Paul Laurence Dunbar

The Hesitating Blues

HELLO, Central, what's the matter with this line?
I want to talk to that high Brown of mine,
Tell me, How long will I have to wait?
Please give me 298. Why do you hesitate?
What you say, "Can't talk to my Brown!
A storm last night blowed the wires all down!"
Tell me how long will I have to wait?
Oh, won't you tell me now? Why do you hesitate?

"Procrastination is the thief of time,"
So all the wise owls say,
"One stitch in time may save nine,"
Tomorrow's not today
And if you put off
Somebody's bound to lose,
I'd be his, he'd be mine,
And I'd be feeling gay.
Left alone to grieve and pine,
My best friend's gone away.
He's gone and left me
The Hesitating Blues.

Sunday night my beau proposed to me;
Said he'd be happy if his wife I'd be,
Said he, "How long will I have to wait?
Come be my wife, my Kate. Why do you hesitate?"

I declined him just for a stall;
He left that night on the Cannon Ball.
Honey, how long will I have to wait?
Will you come back now
Or will you hesitate?

W. C. Handy

(Copyright W. C. Handy 1915)

Puck Goes to Court

I WENT to court last night,
Before me firefly light;
And there was Lady Mab,
On cheek a cunning dab
Of rouge the sun set down,
King Oberon with crown
Of gold-eyed daisy buds
Among potato spuds
Was dancing roundelay
With Lady Chloe and May.

I hid among the flowers
And spent the wee young hours
In mixing up the punch;
For I was on a hunch
That sober men are dull
And fairy dust will lull
To rest the plodding mind
Worn down by life's thick grind.

The nobles drank the brew
And called it sweetest dew;
But when I left they lay
Stunned by the light of day
And Oberon had writ
Decree that I must flit

A hundred leagues from court.
(Alas! Where is there sport?)

Fenton Johnson

Sea Lyric

OVER the seas tonight, love,
   Over the darksome deeps,
Over the seas tonight, love,
   Slowly my vessel creeps.

Over the seas tonight, love,
   Walking the sleeping foam—
Sailing away from thee, love,
   Sailing from thee and home.

Over the seas tonight, love,
   Dreaming beneath the spars—
Till in my dreams you shine, love,
   Bright as the listening stars.

William Stanley Braithwaite

After the Winter

SOME day, when trees have shed their leaves
    And against the morning's white
The shivering birds beneath the eaves
    Have sheltered for the night,
We'll turn our faces southward, love,
    Toward the summer isle
Where bamboos spire the shafted grove
    And wide-mouthed orchids smile.

And we will seek the quiet hill
    Where towers the cotton tree,
And leaps the laughing crystal rill,
    And works the droning bee.
And we will build a cottage there
    Beside an open glade,
With black-ribbed bluebells blowing near,
    And ferns that never fade.

Claude McKay

Guardianship

THAT dusky child upon your knee
Is breath of God's eternity;
Direct his vision to the height—
Let naught obscure his royal right.

Although the highways to renown
Are iron-barred by fortune's frown,
'Tis his to forge the master-key
That wields the locks of destiny!

Georgia Douglas Johnson

To James

Do you remember
How you won
That last race?
How you flung your body
At the start . . .
How your spikes
Ripped the cinders
In the stretch . . .
How you catapulted
Through the tape . . .
Do you remember?
Don't you think
I lurched with you
Out of those starting holes?
Don't you think
My sinews tightened
At those first
Few strides . . .
And when you flew into the stretch
Was not all my thrill
Of a thousand races
In your blood?
At your final drive
Through the finish line
Did not my shout
Tell of the

Triumphant ecstasy
Of victory?
Live
As I have taught you
To run, Boy—
It's a short dash
Dig your starting holes
Deep and firm
Lurch out of them
Into the straightaway
With all the power
That is in you
Look straight ahead
To the finish line
Think only of the goal
Run straight
Run high
Run hard
Save nothing
And finish
With an ecstatic burst
That carries you
Hurtling
Through the tape
To victory. . . .

Frank Horne

VIII. Rain, Flood and Big Water

The Cotton Cat

WITH button eyes and cotton skin
How can a kitten sit and grin?
With skin of striped calico
And only thread between each toe—
I've looked and found out, so I know!

It must feel funny for a cat
To have its tail just painted flat.
But when we're in because of snow
I hold my toy at the window,
And I forget the button eyes
As we both watch the storm and skies.

Mary Effie Lee Newsome

Rain

TODAY the rain
is an aged man
a gray old man
a curious old man
in a music store

Today houses
are strings of a harp
soprano harp strings
bass harp strings
in a music store

The ancient man
strums the harp
with thin long fingers
attentively picking
a weary jingle
a soft jazzy jangle
then dodders away
before the boss comes 'round. . . .

Frank Marshall Davis

Dark Girl

EASY on your drums,
Easy wind and rain,
And softer on your horns,
She will not dance again.

Come easy little leaves
Without a ghost of sound
From the China trees
To the fallow ground.

Easy, easy drums
And sweet leaves overhead,
Easy wind and rain;
Your dancing girl is dead.

Arna Bontemps

Sailor

HE SAT upon the rolling deck
Half a world away from home,
And smoked a Capstan cigarette
And watched the blue waves tipped with foam.

He had a mermaid on his arm,
An anchor on his breast,
And tattooed on his back he had
A blue bird in a nest.

Langston Hughes

The Wakeupworld

This was the song of the Wakeupworld,
The beautiful beast with long tail curled:

"Wake up, O World; O World, awake!
The light is bright on hill and lake;
O World, awake; wake up, O World!
The flags of the wind are all unfurled;
Wake up, O World; O World, awake!
Of earth's delightfulness partake.

Wake up, O World, whatever hour;
Sweet are the fields, sweet is the flower!
Wake up, O World; O World, awake;
Perhaps to see the daylight break,
Perhaps to see the sun descend,
The night begin, the daylight end.

But something surely to behold,
Not bought with silver or with gold,
Not shown in any land of dreams.
For open eyes the whole world teems
With lovely things to do or make,
Wake up, O World; O World, awake!"

Such was the song of the Wakeupworld,
The beautiful beast with long tail curled,

The Wakeupworld so swift and fleet,
With twelve bright eyes and six strong feet.
Such was the song he sang all day,
Lest man or beast should sleep away
The gift of Time, and never know
The beauties of this life below.
Twelve were his eyes, as I have said,
Placed clockwise in his massive head.
Never in any time or weather
Were all those eyes shut tight together,
But daily, at its certain hour,
Each eye became possessed of power.

At one, an eye all pale and white
Flew open for the day's first sight,
And looked alone until at two
There woke his wondering eye of blue.
His eye of green at stroke of three
Blazed like a jewel brilliantly;
At four he opened up the red,
And all around its lustre spread.
Shyly then, as if all sleepy yet,
At five peeped forth the violet.
An eye of silver, chill and cold,
The hour of six would then unfold.
At seven with a sudden wink,
He would let loose his eye of pink.
At eight an eye so mild and mellow

Would gaze about; this one was yellow.
Prompt at the stroke of nine they say
Would twinkle forth his eye of gray.
At ten, as merry as a clown,
You could behold the laughing brown.
Eleven strikes! And open flies
An eye as black as midnight skies.
And when the hour of twelve was tolled,
And Time was one more half day old,
He opened full his eye of gold.
His twelve bright eyes he flashed around
Till rainbows flecked the trees and ground!
Oh, loveliest beast in song or story,
The Wakeupworld in all his glory!

He could not sleep as others could;
But for a moment in the wood
Might stand and rest himself a mite,
Then quickly would be off in flight,
Crossing mountain, field, and lake,
Bidding the drowsy world awake.
Every hour some sleepyhead
Would hear his song and leap from bed
To open his eyes on some delight
Of lovely day or beauteous night.

What would *you* give to see alive
A Wakeupworld at half past five?

Could anything excite you more
Than seeing him at exactly four,
His eyes of white, blue, green, and red,
Leaping like carlights from his head?
Or watch each eye from hour to hour,
Beginning at exactly one,
Unfold its beauty like a flower,
Till all those eyes were on the sun?
'Twould take you half a day at least
To get the most of such a feast!
(He'd be the prize of any Zoo,
If he were here, I think, don't you?)
But never shall his like appear
Again, and we shall never hear
His song in lovely measures hurled
At sleepyheads throughout the world.

Excitement robbed him of his breath,
Excitement led him to his death.
Flood morning when he could have been
(Being awake) the first one in,
Excitement made him play the dunce
And open all his eyes at once!
He rushed right on through dawn and dark
Pointing late comers to the Ark.
Too great the strain was for his heart;
Slowly he sank; his great knees shook.
While those his song had helped to start
Passed on without a backward look.

The waters fell upon him there,
His twelve bright eyes shining like one;
They covered him, and none knew where
To find him when the storm was done.

Countee Cullen

In Time of Silver Rain

IN TIME of silver rain
The earth
Puts forth new life again,
Green grasses grow
And flowers lift their heads,
And over all the plain
The wonder spreads
Of life, of life, of life!

In time of silver rain
The butterflies lift silken wings
To catch a rainbow cry,
And trees put forth
New leaves to sing
In joy beneath the sky
As down the roadway passing boys
And girls go singing, too,
In time of silver rain
When spring
And life are new.

Langston Hughes

IX. Dressed Up

When Sue Wears Red

WHEN Susanna Jones wears red
Her face is like an ancient cameo
Turned brown by the ages.

Come with a blast of trumpets,
    Jesus!

When Susanna Jones wears red
A queen from some time-dead Egyptian night
Walks once again.

Blow trumpets, Jesus!

And the beauty of Susanna Jones in red
Burns in my heart a love-fire sharp like pain.

Sweet silver trumpets,
    Jesus!

Langston Hughes

"Little Brown Boy"

LITTLE brown boy,
Slim, dark, big-eyed,
Crooning love songs to your banjo
Down at the Lafayette—
Gee, boy, I love the way you hold your head,
High sort of and a bit to one side,
Like a prince, a jazz prince. And I love
Your eyes flashing, and your hands,
And your patent-leathered feet,
And your shoulders jerking the jig-wa.
And I love your teeth flashing,
And the way your hair shines in the spotlight
Like it was the real stuff.
Gee, brown boy, I love you all over.
I'm glad I'm a jig. I'm glad I can
Understand your dancin' and your
Singin', and feel all the happiness
And joy and don't-care in you.
Gee, boy, when you sing, I can close my ears
And hear tomtoms just as plain.
Listen to me, will you, what do I know
About tomtoms? But I like the word, sort of,
Don't you? It belongs to us.
Gee, boy, I love the way you hold your head,
And the way you sing and dance,
And everything.

Say, I think you're wonderful. You're
All right with me,
You are.

Helene Johnson

Red

SHE went to buy a brand new hat,
And she was ugly, black, and fat:
"This red becomes you well," they said,
And perched it high upon her head.
And then they laughed behind her back
To see it glow against the black.
She paid for it with regal mien,
And walked out proud as any queen.

Countee Cullen

Dressed Up

I HAD ma clothes cleaned
Just like new.
I put 'em on but
I still feels blue.

I bought a new hat,
Sho is fine,
But I wish I had back that
Old gal o' mine.

I got new shoes—
They don't hurt ma feet,
But I ain't got nobody
For to call me sweet.

Langston Hughes

Oh, Dem Golden Slippers

Oh, my golden slippers am laid away,
Kase I don't 'spect to wear 'em till my weddin' day,
An' my long tail'd coat, dat I love so well,
  I will wear up in de chariot in de morn.
An' my long, white robe dat I bought las' June,
I'm gwinter get it changed kase it fits too soon,
An' de old gray horse dat I used to drive
  I will hitch up to de chariot in de morn.

  Oh, dem golden slippers!
  Oh, dem golden slippers!
  Golden slippers I'm gwinter wear,
  Because dey look so neat;
  Oh, dem golden slippers!
  Oh, dem golden slippers!
  Golden slippers I'm gwinter wear,
  To walk de golden streets.

Oh, my old banjo hangs on de wall,
Kase it ain't been tuned since way las' fall.
But de darkies all say we will have a good time,
  When we ride up in de chariot in de morn.
Dere's old Brother Ben an' Sister Luce,
Dey will telegraph de news to Uncle 'Bacco Juice,
What a great camp meetin' dere will be dat day.
  When we ride up in de chariot in de morn.

Oh, dem golden slippers!
Oh, dem golden slippers!
Golden slippers I'm gwinter wear,
Because dey look so neat;
Oh, dem golden slippers!
Oh, dem golden slippers!
Golden slippers I'm gwinter wear,
To walk de golden streets.

Oh, my good-by, children, I will have to go,
Where de rain don't fall or de wind don't blow,
An' you' ulster coats, why, you will not need,
    When you ride up in de chariot in de morn.
But de golden slippers mus' be neat an' clean,
An' yo' age mus' be jes' sweet sixteen,
An' yo' white kid gloves you will have to wear,
    When you ride up in the chariot in de morn.

Oh, dem golden slippers!
Oh, dem golden slippers!
Golden slippers I'm gwinter wear,
Because dey look so neat;
Oh, dem golden slippers!
Oh, dem golden slippers!
Golden slippers I'm gwinter wear,
To walk de golden streets.

James A. Bland

X. Big Cities

The Zulu King: New Orleans

(At Mardi Gras)

THE ZULU King arrived at the new Basin
Canal in his royal barge,
Profusely decorated with palms and
Surrounded by his brave warriors;
A robust crew, with skin as glossy as
Black satin.
They were robed in tawny tiger skins
Armed with fantastic shields
And pointed menacing spears.
The barbaric floats passed in review,
A majestical parade.
Cheers rose from thousands of loyal
Subjects on Rampart Street.
On one float stood a huge ebony kettle
Containing a naked pot-bellied babe
Simmering over a mock bush fire.
Tom-toms beat a steady monotonous tune.
They stirred long buried savage impulses.
The blood quickened in my pagan heart;
Africa called to her own again.

Josephine Copeland

Bottled: New York

UPSTAIRS on the third floor
Of the 135th Street library
In Harlem, I saw a little
Bottle of sand, brown sand
Just like the kids make pies
Out of down at the beach.
But the label said: "This
Sand was taken from the Sahara desert."
Imagine that! The Sahara desert!
Some bozo's been all the way to Africa to get some sand.

And yesterday on Seventh Avenue
I saw a Negro dressed fit to kill
In yellow gloves and swallow-tail coat
And twirling a cane. And everyone
Was laughing at him. Me too,
At first, till I saw his face
When he stopped to hear a
Organ grinder grind out some jazz.
Boy! You should a seen that fellow's face!
It just shone. Gee, he was happy!
And he began to dance. No
Charleston or Black Bottom for him.
No sir. He danced just as dignified
And slow. No, not slow either.
Dignified and *proud!* You couldn't

Call it slow, not with all the
Cuttin' up he did. You would a died to see him.

The crowd kept yellin' but he didn't hear,
Just kept on dancin' and twirlin' that cane
And yellin' out loud every once in a while.
I know the crowd thought he was coo-coo.
But say, I was where I could see his face,
And somehow, I could see him dancin' in a jungle,
A real honest-to-goodness jungle, and he wouldn't have
    on them
Trick clothes—those yellow shoes and yellow gloves
And swallow-tail coat. He wouldn't have on nothing.
And he wouldn't be carrying no cane.
He'd be carrying a spear with a sharp fine point
Like the bayonets we had "over there."
And the end would be dipped in some kind of
Hoodoo poison. And he'd be dancin' black and naked
    and gleaming.
And he'd have rings in his ears and on his nose
And bracelets and necklaces of elephants' teeth.
Gee, I bet he'd be beautiful then all right.

No one would laugh at him then, I bet.
Say! That man that took that sand from the Sahara
    desert
And put it in a little bottle on a shelf in the library,

That's what they done to this dancer, ain't it? Bottled
  him.
Trick shoes, trick coat, trick cane, trick everything—all
  glass—
But inside—
Gee, that poor guy!

Helene Johnson

When Dawn Comes to the City: New York

THE tired cars go grumbling by,
    The moaning, groaning cars,
And the old milk carts go rumbling by
    Under the same dull stars.
Out of the tenements, cold as stone,
    Dark figures start for work;
I watch them sadly shuffle on,
    'Tis dawn, dawn in New York.

But I would be on the island of the sea,
    In the heart of the island of the sea,
Where the cocks are crowing, crowing, crowing,
And the hens are cackling in the rose-apple tree,
Where the old draft-horse is neighing, neighing, neigh-
            ing
    Out on the brown dew-silvered lawn,
And the tethered cow is lowing, lowing, lowing,
And dear old Ned is braying, braying, braying,
And the shaggy Nannie goat is calling, calling, calling
    From her little trampled corner of the long wide lea
That stretches to the waters of the hill-stream falling
        Sheer upon the flat rocks joyously!
    There, oh there! on the island of the sea,
        There I would be at dawn.

The tired cars go grumbling by,
    The crazy, lazy cars,
And the same milk carts go rumbling by
    Under the dying stars.
A lonely newsboy hurries by,
    Humming a recent ditty;
Red streaks strike through the gray of the sky,
    The dawn comes to the city.

    But I would be on the island of the sea,
    In the heart of the island of the sea,
  Where the cocks are crowing, crowing, crowing,
  And the hens are cackling in the rose-apple tree,
Where the old draft-horse is neighing, neighing, neigh-
            ing
    Out on the brown dew-silvered lawn,
  And the tethered cow is lowing, lowing, lowing,
And dear old Ned is braying, braying, braying,
And the shaggy Nannie goat is calling, calling, calling
  From her little trampled corner of the long wide lea
That stretches to the waters of the hill-stream falling
    Sheer upon the flat rocks joyously!
    There, oh there! on the island of the sea,
        There I would be at dawn.

                                        Claude McKay

The Tropics in New York: New York

BANANAS ripe and green, and ginger-root,
  Cocoa in pods and alligator pears,
And tangerines and mangoes and grape fruit,
  Fit for the highest prize at parish fairs,

Set in the window, bringing memories
  Of fruit-trees laden by low-singing rills,
And dewy dawns, and mystical blue skies
  In benediction over nun-like hills.

My eyes grew dim, and I could no more gaze;
  A wave of longing through my body swept,
And, hungry for the old, familiar ways,
  I turned aside and bowed my head and wept.

Claude McKay

Trip: San Francisco

I WENT to San Francisco.
I saw the bridges high
Spun across the water
Like cobwebs in the sky.

Langston Hughes

City: San Francisco

In the morning the city
Spreads its wings
Making a song
In stone that sings.

In the evening the city
Goes to bed
Hanging lights
About its head.

Langston Hughes

Dawn Patrol: Chicago

NIGHT creeps over the city;
Streets spangle with kilowatt pearls,
Lights splatter over seas of shadows
Damming the flood of darkness.
Drunken night,
A hobo bowed over a bar of time,
Brooding over a black bottle of stars
Blinking like beer bubbles.
Soon comes the police patrol of dawn,
Night slowly staggers away
And then the day.

Richard V. Durham

Havana Dreams: Havana

THE dream is a cocktail at Sloppy Joe's—
(Maybe—nobody knows.)

The dream is the road to Batabano.
(But nobody knows if that is so.)

Perhaps the dream is only her face—
Perhaps it's a fan of silver lace—
Or maybe the dream's a Vedado rose—
(Quien sabe? Who really knows?)

Langston Hughes

Tenement Room: Chicago

BRUISED and battered
By the dark silent hammers of night,
The day creeps
Slowly
From the tired room.

Dirt and destitution
Lounge here in gaudy tatters
Through the bright hours,
Forever shouting
Its bony nakedness—
A crippled table, gray from greasy water;
Two drooping chairs, spiritless as wounded soldiers
        shoved into a prison hole;
A cringing bed, age-weary;
Corseted with wire, squats a flabby stove;
In this corner slumps a punished trunk;
Through the lone window, broken-paned, light and
        weather spill on the dust-defeated and splintered
        floor.

Only night muffles
These visual cries
Of the despairing room.

The dusk
Lays a soothing hand

On its whimpering poverty;
Even the solitary gas jet
Eases its quivering runners
Of chromium light
Along quiet surfaces
As
Exhausted
The room sleeps dreamlessly. . . .

Frank Marshall Davis

Incident: Baltimore

Once riding in old Baltimore,
  Heart-filled, head-filled with glee,
I saw a Baltimorean
  Keep looking straight at me.

Now I was eight and very small,
  And he was no whit bigger,
And so I smiled, but he poked out
  His tongue, and called me, "Nigger."

I saw the whole of Baltimore
  From May until December;
Of all the things that happened there
  That's all that I remember.

Countee Cullen

Rulers: Philadelphia

It is said that many a king in troubled Europe would
   sell his crown for a day of happiness.
I have seen a monarch who held tightly the jewel of
   happiness.
On Lombard Street in Philadelphia, as evening dropped
   to earth, I gazed upon a laborer duskier than a sky
   devoid of moon. He was seated on a throne of flour
   bags, waving his hand imperiously as two small
   boys played on their guitars the ragtime tunes of
   the day.
God's blessing on the monarch who rules on Lombard
   Street in Philadelphia.

Fenton Johnson

Song of Hannibal: Rome

(Near the Gates of Rome)

Out of the land of the burning sun—
From Africa I come.
Through the Alpine snow,
To great Rome I go,
And we halt when the goal is won—
We shall camp in the streets of Rome.
And where is her great army—
Is each man safe at home?
Ha! Ha! They dare not bar me!
To Rome! On to Rome!

I knock
And stand at your door and mock;
So open wide the door,
Or I shall burn and maim and slay
Through Rome forevermore—
Through Rome forevermore!

Whelp of the Lion of Carthage am I—
Born of the Lion's Brood;
And these men of silk—
Will they give me milk
When for nice, warm blood I cry—
When I cry for nice, warm blood?

At the shrine of the Gods did I swear it
Beneath my father's hand,
With fire and sword to tear it—
This land that would crush our land.

I laugh
And your warriors fly like chaff—
Dost, thus, thou me defy?
Then die—die—die—die—die—
Ye dogs of Rome must die!—
Ye dogs of Rome must die!

Marcus B. Christian

Heaven: The City Called Heaven

HEAVEN is
The place where
Happiness is
Everywhere.

Animals
And birds sing—
As does
Everything.

To each stone,
"How-do-you-do?"
Stone answers back,
"Well! And you?"

Langston Hughes

XI. North and South

The Spanish Needle

LOVELY dainty Spanish needle
  With your yellow flower and white,
Dew bedecked and softly sleeping,
  Do you think of me tonight?

Shadowed by the spreading mango,
  Nodding o'er the rippling stream,
Tell me, dear plant of my childhood,
  Do you of the exile dream?

Do you see me by the brook's side
  Catching crayfish 'neath the stone,
As you did the day you whispered:
  Leave the harmless dears alone?

Do you see me in the meadow
  Coming from the woodland spring
With a bamboo on my shoulder
  And a pail slung from a string?

Do you see me all expectant
  Lying in an orange grove,
While the swee-swees sing above me,
  Waiting for my elf-eyed love?

Lovely dainty Spanish needle,
    Source to me of sweet delight,
In your far-off sunny southland
    Do you dream of me tonight?

                              Claude McKay

The Snail

LITTLE snail,
Dreaming you go.
Weather and rose
Is all you know.

Weather and rose
Is all you see,
Drinking the dewdrop's
Mystery.

Langston Hughes

The Unknown Color

I've often heard my mother say,
When great winds blew across the day,
And, cuddled close and out of sight,
The young pigs squealed with sudden fright
Like something speared or javelined,
"Poor little pigs, they see the wind."

Countee Cullen

Dust Bowl

THESE were our fields.
Now no flower blooms,
No grain grows here
Where earth moves in every wind.

No birds nest in these trees.
No fruit hangs
Where the boughs stretch bare
In the sun.

The dust sifts down—blows in.
Our mouths are filled.
The dust moves across,
And up and around the dust moves

In our waking—our sleeping—
In our dreams.

Robert A. Davis

Northboun'

O' DE wurl' ain't flat,
An' de wurl' ain't roun',
Hit's one long strip
Hangin' up an' down—
Jes Souf an' Norf;
Jes Norf an' Souf.

Talkin' 'bout sailin' 'roun' de wurl'—
Huh! I'd be so dizzy my head 'ud twurl.
If dis heah earf wuz jes' a ball
You know the people all 'ud fall.

O' de wurl' ain't flat,
An' de wurl' ain't roun',
Hit's one long strip
Hangin' up an' down—
Jes Souf an' Norf;
Jes Norf an' Souf.

Talkin' 'bout the City whut Saint John saw—
Chile, you oughta go to Saginaw;
A feller's chance is "finest kind,"
An' pretty gals ain't hard to find.

Huh! de wurl' ain't flat,
An' de wurl' ain't roun',

Jes' one long strip
Hangin' up an' down.
Since Norf is up,
An' Souf is down,
An' Hebben is up,
I'm upward boun'.

Ariel Williams Holloway

North and South

O SWEET are tropic lands for waking dreams!
    There time and life move lazily along.
There by the banks of blue-and-silver streams
    Grass-sheltered crickets chirp incessant song,
Gay-colored lizards loll all through the day,
    Their tongues outstretched for careless little flies,
And swarthy children in the fields at play,
    Look upward laughing at the smiling skies.
A breath of idleness is in the air
    That casts a subtle spell upon all things,
And love and mating-time are everywhere,
    And wonder to life's commonplaces clings.
The fluttering humming-bird darts through the trees
    And dips his long beak in the big bell-flowers,
The leisured buzzard floats upon the breeze,
    Riding a crescent cloud for endless hours,
The sea beats softly on the emerald strands—
O sweet for quiet dreams are tropic lands!

Claude McKay

Drums of Haiti

BEAT—beat—beat—drums—beat;
Beat—beat—throb through the sweltering heat;
Ominous throbbing thunder
  Beating like drums of doom,
Rhythm of pause and wonder,
  Filling the air with gloom;
Beat—beat—beat—drums—beat.

Beat—beat—beat—drums—beat;
Beat—beat—over the cane-fields sweet;
Beat through the sunshine and the rain,
  Throb out your message of glorious birth;
Call through the mountain and the plain
  To black men scattered throughout the earth;
Beat—beat—beat—drums—beat.

Marcus B. Christian

XII. Folks

Sister Lou

Honey
When de man
Calls out de las' train
You're gonna ride,
Tell him howdy.

Gather up yo' basket
An' yo' knittin' an' yo' things,
An' go on up an' visit
Wid frien' Jesus fo' a spell.

Show Marfa
How to make yo' greengrape jellies,
An' give po' Lazarus
A passel of them Golden Biscuits.

Scald some meal
Fo' some rightdown good spoonbread
Fo' li'l box-plunkin' David.

An' sit aroun'
An' tell them Hebrew Chillen
All yo' stories. . . .

Honey
Don't be feared of them pearly gates,

Don't go 'round to de back,
No mo' dataway
Not evah no mo'.

Let Michael tote yo' burden
An' yo' pocketbook an' evahthing
'Cept yo' Bible,
While Gabriel blows somp'n
Solemn but loudsome
On dat horn of his'n.

Honey
Go straight on to de Big House,
An' speak to yo' God
Widout no fear an' tremblin'.

Then sit down
An' pass de time of day awhile.

Give a good talkin' to
To yo' favorite 'postle Peter,
An' rub the po' head
Of mixed-up Judas,
An' joke awhile wid Jonah.

Then, when you gits de chance,
Always rememberin' yo' raisin',
Let 'em know youse tired
Jest a mite tired.

Jesus will find yo' bed for you
Won't no servant evah bother wid yo' room.
Jesus will lead you
To a room wid windows
Openin' on cherry trees an' plum trees
Bloomin' everlastin'.

An' dat will be yours
Fo' keeps.

Den take yo' time . . .
Honey, take yo' bressed time.

Sterling Brown

Aunt Jane Allen

STATE STREET is lonely today. Aunt Jane Allen has driven her chariot to Heaven.

I remember how she hobbled along, a little woman, parched of skin, brown as the leather of a satchel and with eyes that had scanned eighty years of life.

Have those who bore her dust to the last resting place buried with her the basket of aprons she went up and down State Street trying to sell?

Have those who bore her dust to the last resting place buried with her the gentle word *Son* that she gave to each of the seed of Ethiopia?

Fenton Johnson

The Banjo Player

THERE is music in me,
    the music of a peasant people.
I wander through the levee, picking my banjo
    and singing my songs of the cabin and the field.
    At the Last Chance Saloon I am as welcome as the
    violets in March;
    there is always food and drink for me there,
    and the dimes of those who love honest music.
    Behind the railroad tracks the little children
    clap their hands and love me as they love
    Kris Kringle.
But I fear that I am a failure.
    Last night a woman called me a troubadour.
    What is a troubadour?

Fenton Johnson

Alabama Earth

(At Booker Washington's grave)

Deep in Alabama earth
His buried body lies—
But higher than the singing pines
And taller than the skies
And out of Alabama earth
To all the world there goes
The truth a simple heart has held
And the strength a strong hand knows,
While over Alabama earth
These words are gently spoken:
Serve—and hate will die unborn.
Love—and chains are broken.

Langston Hughes

"I Think I See Her"

"I can remember when I was a little, young girl, how my old mammy would sit out of doors in the evenings and look up at the stars and groan, and I would say, 'Mammy, what makes you groan so?' And she would say, 'I am groaning to think of my poor children; they do not know where I be and I don't know where they be. I look up at the stars and they look up at the stars!' "— *Sojourner Truth*

I THINK I see her sitting bowed and black,
    Stricken and seared with slavery's mortal scars,
Reft of her children, lonely, anguished, yet
    Still looking at the stars.

Symbolic mother, we thy myriad sons,
    Pounding our stubborn hearts on Freedom's bars,
Clutching our birthright, fight with faces set,
    Still visioning the stars!

                            Jessie Fauset

For a Lady I Know

SHE even thinks that up in heaven
   Her class lies late and snores,
While poor black cherubs rise at seven
   To do celestial chores.

Countee Cullen

For Paul Laurence Dunbar

Born of the sorrowful of heart
Mirth was a crown upon his head;
Pride kept his twisted lips apart
In jest, to hide a heart that bled.

Countee Cullen

Mother to Son

WELL, son, I'll tell you:
Life for me ain't been no crystal stair.
It's had tacks in it,
And splinters,
And boards torn up,
And places with no carpet on the floor—
Bare.
But all the time
I'se been a-climbin' on,
And reachin' landin's,
And turnin' corners,
And sometimes goin' in the dark
Where there ain't been no light.
So, boy, don't you turn back.
Don't you set down on the steps
'Cause you finds it kinder hard.
Don't you fall now—
For I'se still goin', honey,
I'se still climbin',
And life for me ain't been no crystal stair.

Langston Hughes

After Winter

HE SNUGGLES his fingers
In the blacker loam
The lean months are done with.
The fat to come.

His eyes are set
On a brushwood-fire
But his heart is soaring
Higher and higher.

Though he stands ragged
An old scarecrow,
This is the way
His swift thoughts go,

"Butter beans fo' Clara
Sugar corn fo' Grace
An' fo' de little feller
Runnin' space.

"Radishes and lettuce
Eggplants and beets
Turnips fo' de winter
An' candied sweets.

"Homespun tobacco
Apples in de bin
Fo' smokin' an' fo' cider
When de folks draps in."

He thinks with the winter
His troubles are gone;
Ten acres unplanted
To raise dreams on.

The lean months are done with,
The fat to come.
His hopes, winter wanderers,
Hasten home.

"Butterbeans fo' Clara
Sugar corn fo' Grace
An' fo' de little feller
Runnin' space. . . ."

Sterling Brown

XIII. Sky Pictures

Garment

THE clouds weave a shawl
Of downy plaid
For the sky to put on
When the weather's bad.

Langston Hughes

The Road

Ah, LITTLE road, all whirry in the breeze,
A leaping clay hill lost among the trees,
The bleeding note of rapture streaming thrush
Caught in a drowsy bush
And stretched out in a single singing line of dusky song.
Ah, little road, brown as my race is brown,
Your trodden beauty like our trodden pride,
Dust of the dust, they must not bruise you down.
Rise to one brimming golden, spilling cry!

Helene Johnson

Sky Pictures

SOMETIMES a right white mountain
Or great soft polar bear,
Or lazy little flocks of sheep
Move on in the blue air.
The mountains tear themselves like floss,
The bears all melt away.
The little sheep will drift apart
In such a sudden way.
And then new sheep and mountains come.
New polar bears appear
And roll and tumble on again
Up in the skies so clear.
The polar bears would like to get
Where polar bears belong.
The mountains try too hard to stand
In one place firm and strong.
The little sheep all want to stop
And pasture in the sky,
But never can these things be done,
Although they try and try!

Mary Effie Lee Newsome

Pastorale

A WILLOW tree leans far over the brook
Dipping its branches in the cool water
Like a woman who washes her hair over a deep pool
And muses on her reflection there.

The landscape now is dim and shimmering.
Nature's soul pauses to worship
Like a hooded nun telling her beads
In the twilight of a vast cathedral.

Robert A. Davis

Palace

A SEA shell is a palace
Where many echoes dwell,
And when I listen to them
I know them all quite well.
They are like the ocean's roar
Where the sea shell buried deep
Learns why the sea is always salt,
And spooky shadows creep.

Dorothy Vena Johnson

Cycle

So MANY little flowers
Drop their tiny heads
But newer buds come to bloom
In their place instead.

I miss the little flowers
That have gone away,
But the newly budding blossoms
Are equally gay.

Langston Hughes

The Daybreakers

WE ARE not come to wage a strife
    With swords upon this hill;
It is not wise to waste the life
    Against a stubborn will.
Yet would we die as some have done:
Beating a way for the rising sun.

Arna Bontemps

Winter Sweetness

THIS little house is sugar.
    Its roof with snow is piled,
And from its tiny window
    Peeps a maple-sugar child.

Langston Hughes

Twinkling Gown

THE pale dressed evening star
Puts on, when it is night,
A twinkling yellow gown
In which to shine its light.

It sparkles in the darkness
Like a firefly at play.
But soon it softly fades until
At last we see the day.

I do not really understand
Why in dark night, a star
Should gleam, and then turn dull
When dawn creeps from afar.

Dorothy Vena Johnson

Sight

I SEE skies more bright and blue
Than any skies beheld by you,
I see trees so tall and high
Their green leaves brush against the sky,
I see birds (and hear them sing)
Like rainbows that have taken wing;
I see flowers fairer far
Than any in your garden are,
These lovely sights you'll never find,
Because—my dear, you *see*; I'm *blind*.

Cora Ball Moton

Benediction

Go forth, my son,
Winged by my heart's desire!
Great reaches, yet unknown,
Await
For your possession.
I may not, if I would,
Retrace the way with you,
My pilgrimage is through,
But life is calling you!
Fare high and far, my son,
A new day has begun,
The star-ways must be won!

Georgia Douglas Johnson

XIV. Sleep and Dreams

Lullaby

BEDTIME's come fu' little boys.
   Po' little lamb.
Too tiahed out to make a noise,
   Po' little lamb.
You gwine t' have to-morrer sho'?
Yes, you tole me dat befo',
Don't you fool me, chile, no mo',
   Po' little lamb.

You been bad de livelong day,
   Po' little lamb.
Th'owin' stones an' runnin' 'way,
   Po' little lamb.
My, but you's a-runnin' wil',
Look jes' lak some po' folks chile;
Mam' gwine whup you atter while,
   Po' little lamb.

Come hyeah! you mos' tiahed to def,
   Po' little lamb.
Played yo'se'f clean out o' bref,
   Po' little lamb.
See dem han's now—sich a sight!
Would you evah b'lieve dey's white?
Stan' still twell I wash 'em right,
   Po' little lamb.

Jes' cain't hol' yo' haid up straight,
   Po' little lamb.
Hadn't oughter played so late,
   Po' little lamb.
Mammy do' know whut she'd do,
Ef de chillun's all lak you;
You's a caution now fu' true,
   Po' little lamb.

Lay yo' haid down in my lap,
   Po' little lamb.
Y' ought to have a right good slap,
   Po' little lamb.
You been runnin' roun' a heap.
Shet dem eyes an' don't you peep,
Dah now, dah now, go to sleep,
   Po' little lamb.

Paul Laurence Dunbar

Bats

I'D REALLY hate to go to bed
Just swinging from some wall.
But bats, they say, do just that way.
I'd not wish to at all.
I'd hate to swing down from my toes,
All upside-down, and try to doze.

Mary Effie Lee Newsome

Dreams

HOLD fast to dreams
For if dreams die
Life is a broken-winged bird
That cannot fly.

Hold fast to dreams
For when dreams go
Life is a barren field
Frozen with snow.

Langston Hughes

It's a Long Way

It's a long way the sea-winds blow
    Over the sea-plains blue,—
But longer far has my heart to go
    Before its dreams come true.

It's work we must, and love we must,
    And do the best we may,
And take the hope of dreams in trust
    To keep us day by day.

It's a long way the sea-winds blow—
    But somewhere lies a shore—
Thus down the tide of Time shall flow
    My dreams forevermore.

William Stanley Braithwaite

My Little Dreams

I'M FOLDING up my little dreams
Within my heart tonight,
And praying I may soon forget
The torture of their sight.
For Time's deft fingers scroll my brow
With fell relentless art—
I'm folding up my little dreams
Tonight, within my heart!

Georgia Douglas Johnson

For a Poet

I HAVE wrapped my dreams in a silken cloth,
And laid them away in a box of gold;
Where long will cling the lips of the moth,
I have wrapped my dreams in a silken cloth;
I hide no hate; I am not even wroth
Who found earth's breath so keen and cold;
I have wrapped my dreams in a silken cloth,
And laid them away in a box of gold.

Countee Cullen

SHARON

Acknowledgments

For permission to reprint poems included in *Golden Slippers* gratitude is expressed to all the authors represented and to the following publishers and periodicals:

Dodd, Mead & Company for the selections *The Collected Poems* of Paul Laurence Dunbar. Copyright by Dodd, Mead & Company, Inc.

Harcourt, Brace & Company for selections from *Southern Road* by Sterling A. Brown. Copyright, 1932, by Harcourt, Brace & Company, Inc., and *Harlem Shadows* by Claude McKay. Copyright, 1922, by Harcourt, Brace & Company, Inc.

Harper & Brothers for selections from *Color, Copper Sun* and *The Lost Zoo* by Countee Cullen.

Alfred A. Knopf, Inc. for selections from *The Dreamkeeper* by Langston Hughes; to the *Carmel Pine Cone* for poems by Langston Hughes which were originally published in "The Crow's Nest," and to Mrs. Amy Spingarn for permission to reprint *Florida Road Workers* from *Dear Lovely Death* by Langston Hughes.

The Viking Press, Inc. for selections from *God's Trombones*. Copyright, 1927, and *St. Peter Relates an Incident* by James Weldon Johnson. Copyright, 1917, 1921, 1935, by James Weldon Johnson.

The Handy Brothers Music Company for the lyric of *The Hesitating Blues* by W. C. Handy.

The Atlantic Monthly for *The Serving Girl* by Gladys May Casely Hayford and to *The Commonweal, The Crisis* and *Opportunity* for poems first published in their pages.

And to Onah L. Spencer for the version of *John Henry* here used in part.

[199]

Biographies

JAMES A. BLAND (1854-1911) was born in Flushing, Long Island. His parents were free South Carolina folk from Charleston; and his father, Allen M. Bland, was one of the first American Negroes to hold a college degree. Young Bland attended Howard University in Washington, D. C., and worked as a page boy in the House of Representatives. As a college student he was remembered by his classmates more for his banjo playing than for his scholarship. It seemed only natural that he should become a minstrel man upon leaving school. Old minstrel fans remember him as the tall, dark and very striking bandmaster of the *Georgia Minstrels*, but his greatest fame was won in England. There for twenty years he was end-man in a company of white minstrels. King Edward VII was particularly fond of his performances. When his career as a minstrel ended, James A. Bland was temporarily forgotten. He was penniless when he died in 1911. A quarter of a century later his grave was discovered in the Merion Cemetery outside Philadelphia. It was weed-covered and unkept. Meanwhile, though the world had forgotten the name of James A. Bland, it had not forgotten such songs as "Carry Me Back To Old Virginny" and "Oh, Dem Golden Slippers." A group of the composer's admirers moved his grave, erected a singing tower above it and hailed again the man whose songs are second only to those of Stephen Foster in the hearts of Americans. Fifty-three songs are listed in the Library of Congress under the name of James A. Bland.

ARNA BONTEMPS (1902-) was born in Alexandria, Louisiana, but most of his early years were spent in California. He attended elementary and secondary schools in and around Los Angeles and college at U. C. L. A. and at Pacific Union College, Angwin, California, receiving a degree from the latter in 1923. Since then he has studied at Columbia University in New York City and at the University of Chicago. His books include *God Sends Sunday, Black Thunder* and *Drums at Dusk*, novels, and *You Can't Pet a Possum* and *Sad-Faced Boy*, juveniles. He collaborated with Langston Hughes on *Popo and Fifina: Children of Haiti*, and he is the editor of *Father of the Blues*, the autobiography of W. C. Handy.

WILLIAM STANLEY BRAITHWAITE (1878-) was born in Boston, but his ancestry is British. His father and grandfather were both men of standing in the West Indies. Braithwaite, despite the place of his birth and the classical turn of his mind, is mainly self-educated. He is the author of three volumes of poetry, but he is more widely known as a critic and an anthologist. For a number of years he was on the literary editorial staff of the *Boston Transcript*. More recently he has been a member of the English faculty of Atlanta University. In 1918 he was awarded the Spingarn Medal. His books of poetry are *Lyrics of Life, The House of Falling Leaves* and *Sandy Star and Willie Gee*. His anthologies include *The Book of Elizabethan Verse, The Book of Georgian Verse, The Book of Restoration Verse* and a series of yearly anthologies of magazine verse, begun in 1913. He is also author of *The Lyric Year, The Story of the Great War* and a serialized autobiography.

STERLING A. BROWN (1901-) was born in Washington, D. C. He went to public schools in that city. Later he attended Williams College, where he was elected to Phi Beta Kappa in his junior year. After graduation he went to Harvard University for an M.A. This required only one year. Since then he has had a distinguished career as a professor of English, principally at Howard University. His writing has kept pace. His first published book, a volume of poems called *Southern Road*, won him a Guggenheim fellowship. He has since written several books of criticism dealing with the Negro in American literature. He served as adviser on Negro studies in the Federal Writers' Project. That he is still in the midst of widespread creative and scholarly activities is indicated by the simultaneous announcement of three new books by him, books ranging from an anthology of writings by Negroes to a book of observations on the Southern scene.

Marcus B. Christian (1900-   ) was born near Houma, Louisiana, the fourth child in a family of six. His father was a rural school teacher. His grandfather had been a director of public schools in Lafourche Parish during the Reconstruction. So it is not strange that one of Christian's first memories should be of his father reading poetry to the children of the family in French. It was at his father's school that he acquired most of his early education. When the boy was thirteen, however, things took a turn. His father died, as his mother had a few years earlier, and Christian went to work. In 1917 he moved to New Orleans with his brothers and sister. Since then he has attended night schools and taken advantage of some private coaching. There is some good evidence that he made the most of both. He worked as a chauffeur for several years in New Orleans. Later he conducted a cleaning and pressing business. He closed the business in 1936—thanks to the depression—and entered the Federal Writers' Project. In time he was made a Unit Supervisor. He is fond of music, books, old documents and dogs, but his special love is

Louisiana and Negro history. On the side, he does competent bone-carving, wood-work, bookbinding, printing, linoleum block work and work in copper and brass. His poems have appeared in many periodicals.

JOSEPHINE COPELAND was born in Covington, Louisiana, a small resort about sixty miles from New Orleans. The fifth child in a family of six, and living in a community where the school term was short, her education was gained with difficulty. But she loved to read from childhood. Neighbors let her borrow their books, and in time she passed the entrance examination to McDonagh 35 High School in New Orleans. Mornings and evenings, before and after school, she worked. After graduation she attended evening classes at Dillard University and completed a two-year teacher's training course. Lately she has made her home in Chicago.

COUNTEE CULLEN (1903-   ) has been winning laurels since he was a child. Born and educated in New York City, he won enough scholastic medals and citations to decorate a rather stout general. In high school he was a stand-out, and one of his first poems, "I Have a Rendezvous With Life," not only won a city-wide contest, but was quoted from prominent pulpits and reprinted many times. It was as a college student at New York University, however, that Cullen won a real place among American poets. So loud and hearty were the voices raised in praise of his magazine contributions that he almost stole the spotlight from an undefeated football team. The college paper published an article comparing the achievements of the two. Cullen's Phi Beta Kappa key was a foregone conclusion; it surprised no one. His first book of poems appeared the year he graduated. The next year he went to Harvard

University for his M.A. Then followed a Harmon Gold Award for literature, second and third books of poems, a Guggenheim fellowship, two years in Europe and more books. In recent years he has taught French in the schools of New York City. He is the author of *Color, Copper Sun, Ballad of the Brown Girl, Caroling Dusk, The Black Christ, The Medusa and Some Poems, One Way to Heaven* and (with Christopher Cat) *The Lost Zoo*.

WARING CUNEY (1906-   ) has a musical background. Born in Washington, D. C., he attended the public schools of his native city. Later he went to Howard and Lincoln Universities. At Lincoln he became interested in singing, and his work in the Glee Club and the Quartet encouraged further study. Later he studied voice at the New England Conservatory of Music in Boston. A chance meeting with Langston Hughes on a street car in Washington seems to mark the starting point of his writing. Which only goes to show that poetry is "catching." Cuney's poem "No Images" won a first prize in an *Opportunity* contest. He has since contributed frequently to periodicals and anthologies. He lives in New York City.

WESLEY CURTRIGHT's mother brought her children to Harlem when he was just ready for high school. One of his first acts in that new and wonderful environment was the following autobiographical fragment:

> I was born in Brunswick, Georgia,
> Beside the seashore fair;
> Born in Brunswick, Georgia,
> And would like to go back there,
>
> To visit old, old Brunswick,
> That birthplace of mine.

But to think of going there to live,
I should now decline.

A brilliant student, college was interrupted for him by the depression. He is now a clerk in the New York State Civil Service, but his leisure is devoted to solitude and quiet study: books are a-birthing. The date of his birth: November 30, 1910.

FRANK MARSHALL DAVIS (1905-   ) jumped the gun on his teachers and learned to read before entering school at the age of five. Before he was eight he had read *Les Misérables*—both volumes. From then on there was no holding him where books and reading were concerned. He was born in Arkansas City, Kansas, and attended school there till he was ready for Kansas State College. At State College he studied journalism, part of the time on a Sigma Delta Chi scholarship. Big enough to be a football tackle, he spent some of his summers working on farms and with street construction gangs. In 1931 he went to Atlanta and helped to start the *Atlanta Daily World*. He worked as editor of the *World* until 1934. The following year he became feature editor of the Associated Negro Press, a position he still holds. His poetry dates back to his second year in college. Since then it has earned him a Julius Rosenwald Fellowship in poetry and resulted in the publication of several books, among them *Black Man's Verse, I am the American Negro, Through Sepia Eyes* and the forthcoming *47th Street*.

ROBERT A. DAVIS (1917-   ) was born in Mobile, Alabama. Seven years later the family moved to Chattanooga, Tennessee. After another seven years, both parents having died, the children were taken to Chicago to live with relatives. It was as a high school student in that northern city that young Davis commenced writing poetry. He has since contributed to numerous periodicals and given successful public readings of his lyrics. Interested in the theatre, he has taken acting, singing and dancing parts in various amateur productions in the Chicago area. He graduated from the Wendell Phillips high school and has had one year at the University of Chicago and a semester at the Chicago Christian Junior College.

PAUL LAURENCE DUNBAR (1872-1906) was an elevator boy in Dayton, Ohio, when he began writing the poems which made him famous. Before long he found that he had written enough to make a small volume. These he collected under the title *Oak and Ivy* and then published them in book form at his own expense. This was a humble start for the poet, and nothing much came of it; but two years later, when his second book was ready, Dunbar found that he had won friends and supporters. Moreover, William Dean Howells wrote a remarkable criticism of the poems for *Harper's Weekly* and thereby brought the young poet to the attention of American readers in general. That put Dunbar on the ladder. From then on he climbed steadily. Book followed book. He was a hard worker. He wrote "Clorinda" for the Broadway musical stage. He contributed short stories to *The Saturday Evening Post*. He wrote novels. He traveled abroad, and he won the friendship of men like Coleridge Taylor, Booker T. Washington and Frederick Douglass. But most important of all, he continued to write the kind of poetry that the world had come to expect of him. The sum of his work seems large when it is recalled that he died at thirty-three. Born in Dayton, he was educated in the public schools of that city. In high school he was chosen editor of the school paper. He graduated just before his nineteenth birthday. Dunbar's books of poetry include, in addition to *Oak and Ivy, Majors and Minors, Lyrics of Lowly Life, Lyrics of the Hearthside, Lyrics of Sunshine and Shadow,* several illustrated editions of these volumes and the *Collected Poems.* His novels, *The Uncalled, The Fanatics, The Love of Landry* and *The Sport of the Gods.*

RICHARD V. DURHAM (1917-) can hold his own in a boxing ring. He won a sectional championship and an impressive medal in a Chicago Golden Gloves tournament a few years ago. During the two years that followed he boxed as a professional. By that time he had begun writing poems, one of which, "Cotton Croppers," won second prize in a poetry contest sponsored by Mundelien College and Northwestern University. With the poetry prize in one hand, as it were, and the Golden Gloves medal in the other, the boy made his decision in favor of poetry. Since that time he has been attending Northwestern, contributing poems to magazines and newspapers and pursuing an ambition to become a writer of radio scripts. He was born in Jackson, Mississippi. When Durham was ten years old his parents moved to Chicago with their eight children. There he attended the Frances Willard school and Hyde Park High.

JESSIE FAUSET was born and educated in Philadelphia. She later went to Cornell University and remained long enough to earn a B.A. and a Phi Beta Kappa key. At the University of Pennsylvania she took another degree. Then came a period of teaching in the Dunbar High School in Washington, D. C. Later she served as literary editor of *The Crisis.* Interspersed through these activities was a good bit of European travel. She now lives in Montclair, New Jersey, and teaches French in the public schools of New

York City. Miss Fauset has written many poems, but she is perhaps more widely known for her novels, among them *There is Confusion, Plum Bun, The Chinaberry Tree* and *Comedy: American Style.*

GLADYS MAY CASELY HAYFORD (1904-   ) was born at Axim on the African Gold Coast. Her mother was the daughter of the first Judge of the Excommission Court of Sierra Leone, and her father was one of the three first lawyers of the Gold Coast. She is by birth a Fanti, of the tribe which spreads from Axim on the Gold Coast down to Acera, but she attended Penrohs College, Colwyn Bay in Wales. Returning to Africa after five years in England, she became a schoolteacher in The Girls' Vocational School of Sierra Leone. Absence from her native land had increased her appreciation of the beauty of her people, and she came home convinced that she was meant to write for Africa. This she has done in poems like "Serving Girl" and other contributions to such magazines as *The Atlantic Monthly.*

FRANK HORNE (1899-   ) had an early hankering to write, but it took the encouragement of a friendly editor and a fellow poet to bring him out in the open with it. His ambition was in prose, but his first success was in poetry. He was born in New York City. There he attended the public schools and the College of the City of New York. Readers of his poem "To James" will not be surprised to learn that he won varsity letters as a track man, chalked up a "10 flat" in the hundred yard dash and did the quarter mile in 51 seconds. His first poems were written during those days of athletic achievement. Frank Horne later attended the Northern Illinois College of Ophthalmology, took the degree Doctor of Optometry and practiced in Chicago and New York. In later years he returned to graduate study, this time at the University of Southern California, and earned another doctorate. He won a *Crisis* poetry award with a group of poems in which "To James" was included. He has continued to contribute to various periodicals. At present he is an adviser on racial relations to the United States Housing Authority.

WILLIAM CHRISTOPHER HANDY (1873-   ) is the "father of the blues." He was born in Florence, Alabama. There at the age of fifteen, wearing his father's Prince Albert, he got his start in a minstrel company. Since that day his name has become one of the great names in American music, thanks to such compositions as "Memphis Blues," "Beale Street Blues" and "St. Louis Blues." That he is also a poet is plain to anyone who remembers the words to his songs. He has two books to his credit: *Blues—An Anthology* and *Father of the Blues*, an autobiography.

LANGSTON HUGHES (1902-   ) was born in Joplin, Missouri. He made his bow in literature as class poet in the eighth grade. By the time he was nineteen he had seen a poem of his translated into more than a dozen languages and reprinted scores of times throughout the world. That poem was "The Negro Speaks of Rivers." Several volumes of his poetry have been published since then. Upon these rests one of his two strong claims to fame. The other rests upon an amazingly colorful and eventful life, an indication of which may be gathered from the fact that when he set out to write his autobiography at the age of thirty-seven, he found that one volume wouldn't begin to contain it all. His education, often interrupted, included years at Central High in Cleveland, Columbia University in New York City and Lincoln University in Pennsylvania. His travels have carried him to four of the continents, not to mention a number of islands. He has won a hatful of prizes and awards and fellowships, and he has written moving picture scenarios, radio scripts, song lyrics and successful stage plays. His published books include *The Weary Blues, Fine Clothes to the Jew, The Dreamkeeper, Shakespeare in Harlem,* collections of poetry, and *Not Without Laughter, The Ways of White Folks* and *The Big Sea,* fiction and autobiography. He is co-author with Arna Bontemps of *Popo and Fifina: Children of Haiti.* Langston Hughes is a full-time poet. Even his letters and notes are likely to be in verse—the one that accompanied a group of poems to this anthology, for example:

> Some of these for children,
> And some for older fry.
> You may take your choice
> Since you're as old as I.

DOROTHY VENA JOHNSON is a public schoolteacher in Los Angeles, the city in which she was born. In addition to her regular class work she teaches Journalism and Creative Poetry to various grades. Almost every issue of Nuggets, the bi-monthly magazine of poetry by and for children, carries the contributions of several of her pupils. Her own poems have appeared in anthologies. She was educated in Los Angeles, graduating from the University of Southern California and from Teachers' College of U. C. L. A.

FENTON JOHNSON (1888-   ) has lived most of his life in Chicago, the city of his birth. There he attended public schools and the University of Chicago. After college he taught school one year before turning to the literary activities that have occupied him ever since. During this time he has written for the stage of the old Pekin Theatre of Chicago, worked on newspapers and edited and published small magazines. His poems have appeared in numerous periodicals and anthologies over a number of years. The first collection of them, issued when Johnson was twenty-four, was called *A Little Dreaming*. This was followed by *Visions of the Dusk* and *Songs of the Soil*. There were also two books of prose: *Tales of Darkest America* and *For the Highest Good*.

GEORGIA DOUGLAS JOHNSON was born in Atlanta, Georgia, and educated in the schools of her home city, including Atlanta University, and at Oberlin Conservatory in Ohio. After college she became a schoolteacher. Later, when her husband was appointed Recorder of Deeds under President Taft, she moved to Washington, D. C. There she continues to make her home. She has herself been connected with the Department of Labor and other government agencies in the capital. Her Washington home early became a place where young writers liked to gather on Saturday nights to recite new poems and discuss their work. Her career as a poet began with a childhood admiration for the poems of William Stanley Braithwaite. She has since published four volumes of her poems: *The Heart of a Woman, Bronze, An Autumn Love Cycle* and *The Dreams in Me*.

HELENE JOHNSON was born in Boston. She was educated in the public schools of that city and at Boston University. Later she took courses at Columbia University. She has been in New York periodically since 1926, when as a very young girl, she came down to the big city with a sheaf of poems in her hand. She has been published in magazines as hard to impress as *Vanity Fair*, and her poems have been reprinted widely in anthologies.

James Weldon Johnson (1871-1938) once observed that his life seemed to move in cycles of seven. For seven years he and his brother, J. Rosamond Johnson, were engaged in writing songs and musical plays for the stage. This was followed by a seven year period in which he served as United States Consul, first in Venezuela and then in Nicaragua. Then came two seven-year turns with the National Association for the Advancement of Colored People, as field secretary and then as secretary. The final cycle, however, was broken tragically. James Weldon Johnson was a member of the faculty of Fisk University when he was killed in an automobile accident near his summer home in New England. But long before this accident occurred, he had established himself as one of America's great citizens. Born in Jacksonville, Florida, he had attended first the schools of that city and then Atlanta University. While serving as principal of a Jacksonville school and developing it into a high school, he had studied law and been admitted to the Florida bar. With his brother he had in those days written "Lift Every Voice and Sing," a song which was to become known as the Negro national anthem. He had then gone to New York and commenced the remarkable cycle of activities that made him famous. His books began appearing in 1912. They include *The Autobiography of an Ex-Colored Man, Fifty Years and Other Poems, The Book of American Negro Poetry, The Book of American Negro Spirituals, The Second Book of American Negro Spirituals, Black Manhattan, God's Trombones, Along This Way* and *Negro Americans: What Now?*

Claude McKay (1891-) was born in the hills of Clarendon on the island of Jamaica, the youngest of eleven children. His father was a farmer who raised coffee, cocoa, bananas and sugar cane. An older brother was the village schoolmaster. In this brother's school McKay received the rudiments of his education. In the teacher's home he made the acquaintance of some of the great figures in English literature. At seventeen he won a Jamaica Government Trade Scholarship and was apprenticed to a cabinet-maker and wheelwright. At nineteen he joined the Jamaica Constabulary. At twenty he published his first book of poems, *Songs of Jamaica*. Written in the Jamaica dialect, these at once became popular locally and earned him a medal from the Institute of Arts and Sciences. The next year he journeyed to the United States to attend Tuskegee Institute, but Tuskegee held him only three months. His next stop was Kansas State University, at which he remained two years as a student in the department of agriculture. Then he went to New York and presently gave up the thought of returning to the West Indies. It was about this time that America first became aware of Claude McKay the poet. He began contributing to widely read magazines. In 1919 he was off to Holland, Belgium and England. During a year in London he published *Spring in New Hampshire*. Back in America again, he was given an editorial job by Max Eastman of the *Liberator*. The same year Harcourt, Brace & Company brought out an American edition of his poems under the title *Harlem Shadows*. But McKay was off again, this time to Russia and Germany. He reached Paris at the end of 1923 and fell sick. His slow recovery was followed by a prolonged stay in France which was only recently terminated by a return to New York City. His books of prose include *Home to Harlem, Banjo, Gingertown, Banana Bottom, A Long Way From Home* and *Harlem: Black Metropolis*.

CORA BALL MOTON was born in Quincy, Illinois, the city in which she now lives. She went to public schools in Quincy and Chicago prior to attending Knox College and

Macomb Normal. For a number of years she taught school. She has traveled extensively throughout North America. With her husband, a former professor of mathematics, she now lives in a low cottage on a big expanse of green lawn. Around them grow the trees, hollyhocks and rose bushes that her mother planted many years ago. Advancing blindness has restricted her activities recently, but she still sees things that inspire poetry. She has written a great deal for newspapers and magazines.

BEATRICE M. MURPHY is perhaps best known for her anthology *Negro Voices*, but she is also a regular contributor of book columns to newspapers. She has been a private secretary to an educator, a public stenographer and manager and part owner of a circulating library. She was born in Pennsylvania, but most of her life has been spent in Washington, D. C.

MARY EFFIE LEE NEWSOME would rather not talk about how long it has been since she was a child. She needn't worry, though—considering what she has to remember. She was born in Philadelphia, where her father was editor of a colored newspaper. Later the family moved to Texas, the father having become a bishop. There Effie and her younger sister Consuelo learned to amuse themselves by hitching horned toads to match boxes. In nearby fields they discovered white poppies growing wild, and often they saw great droves of long-horned cattle being driven westward by men on horseback. Later there was another move, when Bishop B. F. Lee was transferred to the district which included Ohio, Pennsylvania and surrounding states. In Ohio the children found other wonders. There were horses to ride, and there was a little red school house with a loud bell on top. Naturally, Effie and Consuelo began writing and drawing pictures to describe the things they saw and did. They sent their work to children's pages of magazines, and before long they were winning prizes. Mrs. Newsome has been contributing to magazines ever since, and most of the time she has been writing about that beautiful childhood. Her most recent book of poems is *Gladiola Garden*.

M. BEAUNURUS TOLESON was born in Moberly, Missouri. He attended Fisk, Lincoln and Columbia Universities. He has written much poetry, some of which has been published in newspapers and magazines. Several times his work has been awarded prizes. At present he is professor of English, Coach of Debating and Director of Dramatics at Wiley College, Marshall, Texas. His debating teams have won laurels in all parts of the country.

ARIEL WILLIAMS HOLLAWAY (1905-   ) is the daughter of a Mobile, Alabama, physician. She attended public schools in her native city and then went to Talladega for College. Later she took a Mus. B. degree from Fisk University and followed this with musical studies at Oberlin Conservatory. She then became a director of music at North Carolina College for Negroes. Her poem "Northboun'" was on everybody's lips in Harlem during 1926, the year it won the *Opportunity* contest.

Index of First Lines

[218]

GOLDEN SLIPPERS

SET IN LINOTYPE FAIRFIELD

FORMAT BY A. W. RUSHMORE

MANUFACTURED BY

THE HADDON CRAFTSMEN

PUBLISHED BY

Harper & Brothers

NEW YORK AND LONDON